# An
# ALPHABET
*of*
# AWFUL
# ANIMALS
*for*
# ADULTS
(to read to their grandchildren)

© Essex Women's Advisory Group 2016

Published by Essex Women's Advisory Group
c/o ECF — Registered Charity No. 3062567.

A CIP catalogue record for this book is available from the British Library.

ISBN 978-0-9567397-3-5

Designed by Peter Dolton, Suffolk.
Printed and bound in Spain under the supervision of MRM Graphics, Winslow, Buckinghamshire.

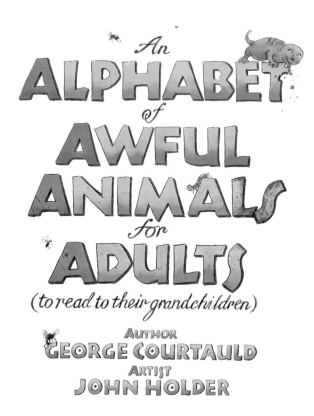

# An ALPHABET of AWFUL ANIMALS for ADULTS

## (to read to their grandchildren)

**AUTHOR**
**GEORGE COURTAULD**
**ARTIST**
**JOHN HOLDER**

EWAG PUBLISHING

*from*

*. . . to*

Hear the busy little **ANT**
huff and puff and gasp and pant.
The little bug is carrying
a large (and rather useless) thing:
an extremely heavy bit
off a chunk of millstone grit;
no wonder it's in such a state
carrying that enormous weight.
And this ANT is not alone
with its burden of that stone,
here's another, on its shoulders
bearing seeds as big as boulders,
whilst another, on its head,
heaves a crumb of mouldy bread.
Several more are carting sticks,
lumps of clay, or even bricks;
all around we hear the pants
of busy little working ANTS:
millions of them, file on file;
let's hope they think it all worth while.

And
while they are working,
you will see, that among
those adorable ANTS
is the long,
sticky tongue
of the 'earth-pig',
(or **AARDVARK**),
an odd-looking beast
which only on ANTS
is delighted to feast.
Which way it goes
is always a doubt:
it has a very fat tail
and a long and thin snout,
so its front end looks sharp,
and its back side looks blunt
which makes the strange AARDVARK
appear back to front.

Regard the graceful **ANTELOPE**.
Unlike the **APE** it does not grope
about to find its neighbour's fleas;
in other ways it tries to please:
its eyes are kind; its speech is meek,
it baths at least four times a week,
its breath is sweet; its thoughts are pure,
its whole demeanour is demure.
The APE will make disgusting faces
and flaunt its rude and private places.
Why is it that, within the zoo,
the APE is whom we'd rather view?

In Araby, land of the Middle East,
among the dunes of sand where camel-shadows roam,
**AL-MI'RAJ** lives: a lonely, friendless little beast.
A cosy, fur-lined burrow is his home;
he seems a mild and timid, harmless chap,
a bunny rabbit with its fluffy ears and scut.
That docile look is just a devious trap
for, from between those ears, a single spike does jut.
Unlike the spikelet of the unicorn
AL-MI'RAJ has a weapon of attack, a fearsome prong:
a curly whirly, shining, black, sharp-pointed horn
of rapier shape and over two feet long.
His lethal use of this peculiar spear
has caused all desert beasts to live in fear:
for look!
Upon a bone that brute does gnaw!
The horrid thing's a carnivore!

To stop the danger from this rabbit
tip-toe behind it, quickly grab it,
then deftly slip
a cork upon its pointed tip.

Most of the insects take offence
at the **BOMBARDIER BEETLE'S** way of defence:
an acidic squirt (which doesn't half hurt),
a terrific bang and a hideous smell
is the BOMBARDIER BEETLE'S way to repel.
Rudest of all, in the opinion of some,
is that he does all this from the tip of his bum.

The BEETLE however, has a friend
who admires the use of this rather rude end –
the **BOLL WEEVIL,** a wretched little creature
who has absolutely no redeeming feature.
So to compensate for its lack of appeal
it follows closely at the BEETLE'S heel
and if ever the BOMBARDIER BEETLE starts
with its awful squirts and frightful farts
the weevil smiles, because he is sure he
is basking in the BOMBARDIER'S reflected glory.

The **BLATANT BEAST** had many tongues and with them he was able
to talk the speech of all mankind as of the tower of Babel.
To Adam and to Eve he spoke in uncouth grunts and snarls,
he warbled in the sing-song speech of old neanderthals,
He'd talk in parlance now obscure like Cornish and Sumerian;
he'd pray in Geez and swear in Manx, he'd even speak Hungarian.
In random speech, he would reply, to questions one might ask,
in Japanese or French or Cree and sometimes ancient Basque.
The language of the fairies most fluently he spoke,
he'd incant secret curses known to the elfin folk.
With serenades, like choristers, so sweetly could he sing;
but dire malignance! – Every tongue concealed a poisonous sting.

When your eyes meet the eyes of a boiled cod, it is said,
the optic exchange carries no peril or risk:
how remarkably different it is, if instead
you encounter the eyes of the grim **BASILISK**.

For when you see the BASILISK
you're in for a big surprise
if, by some unhappy chance,
you happen to catch its eyes:
you'll go all of a-tremble
and feel quite dizzy and ill,
for this fabulous beast
has looks which can kill.

The **CH'WAWA**, and the **CORGI**, and the **COLLIE**
have several reasons to be melancholy;
as, indeed, have the Pug, the Poodle and the Peke:
some people say that each one is a freak:
tho' from the wolf it did originate
evolved it has into a sorry state
of drooping ears, and corkscrew tails, and spots,
knock-kneed, bow-legged, with lots
of nervous habits:
peevish yaps,
slobbery laps,
dripping chaps,
angry snaps
at postmen's legs, and servile begs for bikkies
followed by a heap of sick. He's
a weirdo, is the urban pet.
And so,
it may never end
the mischief man will make to
'Man's Best Friend'.

The CORGI sits beneath a throne
nibbling at a marrow bone,
when he wants to raise a laugh
he nips a footman in the calf.
The COLLIE spends his working days
watching sheep who laze and graze:
from dawn to dusk he thus remains
in the Northern British rains.
The
CORGI
is rather jolly,
the
COLLIE
somewhat melancholy.

Tip-toe, upon the dung-heap, stands the **COCK**
and crows in crass defiance to the sun;
with wifely inattention grubs his flock –
they let him have his little bit of fun.

The hens peck on, all knowing
that though for praise he begs,
it's the cock who does the crowing,
but the hens who lay the eggs.

When all the creatures of the world
are finally created
and, so that there are two of them,
with prudence, duplicated,
the Great Creator deftly fits
together the remaining bits
which, to the surprise of us,
becomes the **DUCK-BILLED PLATYPUS**.

Like the mole, its body shape and beady little eyes;
like the hare, the russet fur (and similar in size);
a beaver's hard and flattened tail; a hamster's pouch-like cheek;
the webbed feet of an otter and a mallard's horny beak;
poisoned, like an adder's fangs, are spurs upon its legs;
and of the oddest of its ways: the funny thing lays eggs!

The **DRAGON**, like the crocodile, had lines of toothy-pegs
made up into a ghastly smile, and bandy little legs,
he also had a pair of wings, and fire puffed from his snout.
One day he told some villagers to take a Maiden out
and tie her to a wooden post: a tasty sacrifice.
(They did it, but they grumbled that it wasn't very nice).

The Maiden was a bonnie lass
and she was pure and chaste
(the reason being, perhaps, she had
a fifty inches waist).

The DRAGON scrutinised the Maid
and thought: 'she's rather podgy,
I think that I will have her grilled,
if baked, she'll be too stodgy.'

Upon his steed, a knight passed by,
a parfit, gentil fellow;
he saw the DRAGON with the Maid,
with anger did he bellow:
'I say! Look here, you blighter! You ought to be ashamed!
Unsporting are your flames and teeth,'
the gallant chap explained:
'Gadzooks! Poor Maiden Undefiled,
she hasn't got a chance;
I'm so annoyed I am resolved
to pierce you with my lance.'

The startled DRAGON crossly thought:
    'he can't do as he pleases,
we DRAGONS now are classified
    as an endangered species.'
And so the DRAGON thoughtfully quit:
    'I will avoid that fool,
    it is my duty to preserve
    my rare genetic pool'.

The **EXTRA TERRESTRIAL BEING**
has arrived from outer space.
He has hairy arms and jointed legs
and a green and purple face;
from each of his ears
sprout out, on stalks
four pairs of tongues, with prongs, like forks;
rubbery feelers grow round his snout;
he wears his innards inside out
and the ring of glands around his waist
continuously drools a glutinous paste;
he has no mouth but somewhere, beneath,
we hear the grinding of pointed teeth;
he does not talk, instead, he expels
puffs of gas with different smells.
Be polite and friendly, and make no fuss,
for what do you think that he thinks of us?

Self-righteously officious, sanctimonious, smug,
the EARLY BIRD shrills sermons at the crack of dawn
in stern reproof of those who doze a-bed, all warm and snug,
trying to sleep away his reveille of the morn.

"Twit-twit-twitter" it tweets in tedious repetition.
I think it is a chaffinch or some sort of dratted tit.
Will it not compose another musical rendition,
and change its reiteration just a bit?

"Get up you lazy-bones, and stir" calls out the bird:
"I've already had my breakfast of a worm."
But that suggestion inconsistently is absurd:
maybe it is the EARLY BIRD which gets the worm,
but it also is the EARLY WORM which gets the bird.

The **FROG** is eaten by the French.
They cook his legs, but throw the rest away;
in garlic sauce his calves and thighs they drench,
and then add herbs to make a fine display.
The FROG is not so fussy of his lunch:
an uncooked **FLY** he likes to munch.

The **FRESIAN COW** is tame and mild,
the **FRISKY FLEA** is fierce and wild;
in mournful 'MOOS' the cow does call,
the FLEA makes not a sound at all;
the FRESIAN COW chews on its cud,
the Fearsome FLEA will suck on blood;
to move, the FLEA will jump about,
the cow will not, it's much too stout.
But of all of their differences,
the biggest ones are these:
FLEAS *can't* have cows,
but cows *can* have FLEAS.

The **GIRAFFE** –
has a very long throat,
so a very rare laugh,
for when, at last,
the laugh can come out,
the GIRAFFE has forgotten
what the laugh was about.

The **GARGOYLE** can be of any shape or size:
perhaps with horns, or half a dozen eyes,
or pointed ears and nose, or jagged teeth;
and cloven feet beneath
a body made of interlocking scales
ending in a pair of pointed tails.

In spite of these alarming features
GARGOYLES are gentle, helpful creatures:
the intention of their terrifying display
is to frighten trolls and other imps away;
and every mouth's a useful water-spout
so when it rains, it spits the water out.

The **HONEY BEE**
for hours and hours
is busy, visiting the flowers:
pollen it takes, and nectar sips;
it packs the pollen round its hips
whilst in the spaces of its tummy
it pours enormous pools of honey.
When it gets back to its mates
the honey it regurgitates
into something called 'a comb'
which fills the inside of its home.
From thence Aunt Mabel spreads it on
a nicely buttered tea-time scone.

Fond Auntie thinks her spread derives
from flowery meads to busy hives,
but you and I know, that, in fact
it's from a bee's digestive tract.

The portly
**HIPPOPOTAMUS**
moves, on land,
with lots of fuss:
with snorts and grunts
she waddles round,
stamping foot-prints
in the ground.

But when in water, like a trout
she swoops and glides and darts about.

A **HYENA** makes his presence felt
with screams of mirth throughout the veldt.
What is the reason for this joy?
'Tis this –
he finds it funny when he steals
the lion family's hard-earned meals.

Over Afric's dusty plains
the regal lion lives and reigns;
this cat is King, he rules supreme,
all beasts obey his stern regime;
severely, he lays down laws
with forceful use of teeth and claws.
Although they're large, not so his brain:
the stately lion is proud and vain:
(like many of the nobility,
he's flattered into gullibility).

Being the family breadwinner
he's ordered out to catch the dinner.
So in the sun he runs pell-mell
after nifty gnu or fleet gazelle.

When the grizzly deed is done the HYENAS in a pack
come to praise the lion, to pat his back
and tell him what a Mighty Fellow he has been,
of such impressive derring-do they have never seen;
he must be tired after all that running and leaping
they will guard his meal in their safe keeping:
"Oh Mighty One, if Thou goest home and tell Her Maj, then
we your humble serfs will carry the gnu for You to Your royal den."

After a wait of a considerable time
the lion begins to wonder if he may be the victim of a crime;
finally it dawns on him that the HYENAS
have yet again taken him to the cleaners.

Of others' labours the HYENA is a collector:
if he was born a human being
he'd be a tax inspector.

I Caligula, Roman Emperor two thousand years ago,
had a friend, INCITATUS, whom he thought of as his beau.
In the smartest of the districts of the capital of Rome
INCITATUS lived in comfort in a grand but cosy home:
with marble walls, and panelled doors, and floored with Persian tiles,
and serried rows of pillars colonnaded into aisles;
from ivory and porphyry were carved his dinner plates –
he'd have them handed out by slaves when dining with his mates.
Upon his breakfast oat-meal flakes some gold dust would be sprinkled,
and whist he ate the bulbuls sang and running fountains tinkled.
His formal robes and trappingss were dyed into purple hues,
of solid plates of silver were crafted all his shoes.
For INCITATUS, Caligula chose Penelope as mate:
her beauty was unparalleled, her temperament first rate.
Caligula then promoted him to join Seniors in debate
as an important officer – a consul of the state
the Senators were forced to say that none had ever heard
INCITATUS ever speak a rude or foolish word.
Caligula, loosing public trust, was stabbed until he died
and INCITATUS was retired and had to live outside.

He noticed little difference in his way of life, of course,
for INCITATUS was a horse.

The pagans hope that they'll entice
their **IDOL** with a sacrifice:
but though the pagans pray and sing,
their IDOL will not do a thing:
its answer to their songs and praise
is a blank and wooden gaze.
This IDOL
is an idle IDOL.

*Megaloceros giganteus*

The **IRISH ELK** had huge and heavy horns,
two weapons which, though mighty and distinct,
were just as futile as the unicorn's –
for both these beasts have now become extinct.

**J**UMBO was an elephant of a quite enormous size:
whenever he went into competitions
he always won the first prize.
He was run over by a train in 1885
which is one of the reasons that he is no longer alive.

Another reason is that, by now,
he'd probably be dead, anyhow.

The wibbly-wobbly JELLYFISH
makes a most unsavoury dish:
neither jam nor bloater paste
can improve its boring taste;
cooks have tried ingenious ways
with curry, mint, and mayonnaise;
they've sprinkled salt, they've ground out pepper,
(neither makes it any better);
with JELLYFISH there's never been
successful efforts at cuisine.

And what has made it worse to eat
are the stings upon its feet.

The **KANGAROO** hops up and down.
It keeps its baby in a pocket
together with its dressing gown,
its wallet and a locket,
a bit of string, a pencil and
a penknife with a hook,
a bag of sand, a rubber band,
and the latest thriller book;
of the Australian cricket team
there's a coloured photograph,
upon the photo' is inscribed
each Aussie's autograph;
there's a boomerang, a billabong,
a didgery widgery doo,
a witchetty grub, and a frightful pong
from the baby KANGAROO.

Observe the **LION**.
His smile is grim,
his mane is neatly brushed and trim.
In vain he roars,
you can't be bluffed
his tail ends in
a teeny
tuft
!

The **LOCH NESS MONSTER** is well famed
for never being around:
when people take their cameras out
this beastie goes to ground
(actually, I suppose we ought'er
really say it 'goes to water').
Whatever, so often is it missed
I wonder if it *does* exist.

A conference of learned linguists
made interesting verbal lists.
From them they chose the ugliest, and the prettiest,
the most suitable, and the wittiest.

They voted that the most beautiful word:
the one most delightfully heard:
the most melodiously mellifluous from every nation,
of soothing languidity of vowels, of liquid murmuration.
is **LIBELLULE**, the French word for 'dragonfly'.

However I have often admired the **LAMMERGEYER**;
what's more its wingspan of 8 feet
makes the dragonfly at 3 inches seem quite petite.
They said that the second most beautiful word is – DIARRHOEA
'It is not what you know' they said, 'but what you hear.'
They agreed that the ugliest word, without doubt,
is SAUERKRAUT,
and that the most amusing in the English language
is SAUSAGE.

**MINNIE** is a **MARMALADE**,
a stout and idle cat;
I'm afraid she has been spayed:
that's maybe why she's fat.
Her Missus loves her dearly,
her Master not so much:
he says: 'I hope to get the chance
to boot her into touch.
Here in our stylish week-end home,
a classy country house,
in every corner I observe
the droppings of a **MOUSE**.
What is the point, one well may ask,
of that lazy lump of fur?'
To this, our MINNIE'S sole reply
is a bland and shameless purr.

Missus and Master often go,
at the setting of the sun,
to sample cocktails at an inn:
Ye Merry Grouse & Gun.
The naughty MICE then scuttle out:
they sport with gleeful squeals,
they scamper up and down the stairs,
they skip, they sport their heels.
Our MINNIE sourly looks at them
and scornful is her glance.
She thinks: 'they are beneath contempt,
I'll let the blighters prance.

☞ The Fellow hopes that after them
with dire intent I'm running.
By my whiskers! He is wrong:
he's another think a-coming.'
Finally Pussy feels a pang
and ambles out of doors
having, on a table leg,
a-sharpened all her claws.
Now Master has a garden
and in it is a pond
in which some fancy fishes swim:
of them he's very fond.
Some fish are blotched in blues and reds,
some striped, some gold as honey;
whichever, as the Master says:
'they cost me pots of money.'
MINNIE contemplates the pool.
She unsheathes from a paw
a fist of fearsome talons;
she picks the sharpest claw.
A fish observes, with goggle eyes,
a furry feline face:
with due decorum MINNIE says
a brief but pious Grace.
Then 'SWISH',
with one deft movement she winkles out the fish.
Within a trice she's eaten it (it was tasty dish).

The fishy snack, and then a pee, a tight squeeze through her flap –
'The Fellow knows not why I'm stout' she thinks,
then has a nap.

Half a maiden, half a fish:
the **MERMAID** is the sailor's wish.
Whilst of the surging seas she sings,
of icebergs, whales and white gulls wings,
and Northern lights, and Saturn's rings,
and battles fought by water kings,
the sailor dreams of other things.

He dreams that she and he are on a lonely isle
and she is laughing at his repartee
to show two rows of pearls in magic smile
below her shining eyes, blue as the sea.

He dreams of tumbling tresses gold as wrack:
long hair that frames her ivory face as veils
which tumble, loosely coiled, along her back,
down to her tail of iridescent scales.

He dreams of nights of passion 'neath the stars,
to roll and slither eel-like through the tide
whilst moonlight sends its long and silver bars
deep, deep into the waters where they slide.

Alas, his blissful dreamings will be blighted
for, as her true love, he will never be,
a dolphin is to whom her troth is plighted,
a fishy friend to sport with, blithe and free.

The **MINOTAUR** had a head of a bull and the body of a human being;
when observed, people could hardly credit what they were seeing:
they did not have much time to muse before he dragged them to a maze
(where he lived) and on their body parts began to graze.
When not eating people he quite liked a moussaka with olives and lamb mince
followed by a tartlet of crispy pastry topped with honeyed figs and grated quince,
all washed down with some hearty draughts of Retsina
(he thought that the astringency made his mouth feel cleaner).

How the MINOTAUR was conceived I will draw a veil:
there are some things which are completely beyond the pale.

Hush - - - all is still and silent in the night,
but for That Thing
which breathes beneath your bed.
The moon shines dim,
pale green its light:
it slowly blinks cold eyes set in its ghastly head
as quietly staring through the window glass
it slowly sidles sideways through the sky
and lights a shape that creeps upon the grass
towards the house wherein you sleepless lie.
Some shadows flitter, floating over trees:
the **NIGHTMARE** rides, astride a grinning horse of bones
in front, a rout of hunted phantoms flees
behind, a vast and shifting shape that groans
in panic effort to out-run the hounds
who follow it in ever-closing bounds –
closer – closer – closer – closer
you are now that shape which flees in fear
lumbering onward, leaden-footed, hopeless in despair.

The sounds of chase and hunting ebb, the shades depart –
or is the fading murmur the beating of your heart?

The **NAKED MOLE-RAT** is completely bare
but for a whisker scattered here and there;
he has a sallow, pinky-greenish, wrinkled skin,
his legs are short and bowed and very thin,
his eyes are microscopic; he has holes instead of ears,
at one end, his naked, worm-like tail appears,
from his mouth two fangs sprout side-by-side –
big enough to make a walrus swell with pride.

Some people keep them as pets: as the saying sums up well –
*"Better to be loved by a NAKED MOLE-RAT*
*than despised by a gazelle."*

Singing in the dusk of eventide
is the **NIGHTINGALE**,
a rapturous fowl.
Because it has a beauteous song
it trills with pride.
Beware, oh NIGHTINGALE,
the watchful owl.

The **NARWHAL**, like the unicorn,
only has a single horn
(actually, to tell the truth,
it's really an enormous tooth).
With such an implement you might think he'll
use it when eating the delicious winkle:*
prodding it about as a skewer to expel
the winkle from his protective shell.
Not at all:
the winkle is rather small
and the NARWHAL'S prong
is twelve feet long.
In fact, the NARWHAL's favourite dish
is the squidgy cuttlefish.
This is because it does not need much chewing, I deduct,
just sucked.

*\* P.S. Winkle, Rip Van,*
*was not a mollusc,*
*but a man.*

The **OSTRICH** has a vest of fluffy down
and curling feathers ornament her gown:
how elegant and smart is this plumage that the OSTRICH grows
upon her back, around her breast, and sprouting from her parson's nose;
but on her drum-sticks, it appears
a pair of tights is all she wears.

Do not make an anxious fuss
when you find an **OCTOPUS**,
and note eight legs with 20 suckers
which are pouted up in puckers,
so if it wraps you in embrace
you will find on every place
you have 160 kisses.

This is disliked by most of us
tho' not by another OCTOPUS.

The **OOZELUM BIRD** flies back to front –
Up forward, it leads with its toes,
and its eyes are where it *has* been.
It never knows which way it goes,
but where it *was*, it has seen.

Another OOZELUM, of a different sort
had only one wing – it is generally thought –
and as it was missing one of its wings
it flew in rapidly diminishing rings.
And where do you think it eventually went?
Why, poor thing, up its own fundament.

That is why it no longer exists.

This is the **PILCHARD**
who squashed in a tin
is smothered in oil
and horribly thin.
Now he regrets that
he was such a fool
to disobey rules
and stray from
his school.

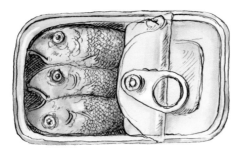

The **PIDDOCK** lives within a shell:
it has a pungent, salty smell;
as well as being rather smelly
it looks just like a blob of jelly,
it cannot sing, it cannot walk,
it cannot see, it cannot talk,
it doesn't think, it doesn't mind,
it isn't nice, nor is it kind;
so why its praises might we sing –
its other name is Angel's Wing.

On the pirate's shoulder,
the **PIRATE'S PARROT** perches.
In stormy water, the pirate's galleon lurches.
Poor PIRATE'S PARROT, in these seas, he
feels rather insecure and ill and queasy.
Off from his shoulder,
does the pirate pick
his PIRATE PARROT,
who is being very sick.

P is for a **PUG DOG** of a very large girth.
She was as fat as a hog from the day of her birth.
With her flat nose and squashed face this PUG
has, it is sad to admit, a most ugly mug.
And her wrinkled brow gives her an air of worried surprise.
But she looks at the world with huge kindly eyes.
With her gentle smile every child she endears:
they love to hug this ugly PUG, and stroke her soft silky ears.
Most people, when meeting this delightful creature
consider she has many a redeeming feature:
her charming nature is the first to come to mind,
not the rather unattractive appearance of her behind –
actually, some of the more fastidious
think that her bottom is absolutely hideous.
Also other people find it rather displeasing
to hear the rasping pant of her perpetual wheezing:
in fact some get quite annoyed
by the audible evidence of her adenoid.
Other people also think it a bit crazy
that this ungainly blob has a dainty name like Daisy.
Her hobby is chasing swifts flying at 60 m.p.h 30 feet overhead.
"A REMARKABLE EXAMPLE OF HOPE OVER REASON"
it is said.

Sometimes, in golden Camelot
when Arthur ruled, he would allot
some knights to do brave deeds
to arm and mount their steeds
and sally out and find the **QUESTING BEAST**.

They quested here, they quested there,
they couldn't find it anywhere:
they searched the seven seas,
down caves, up mossy trees –
no sign of any QUESTING BEAST. ☛

☞ Deaf they must be, maybe blind,
it isn't very hard to find –
80 feet from tail to nose,
a goatling's hooves instead of toes,
eyes like coals, in snake-like head,
instead of teeth it has instead
a treble row of metal spears,
like brazen trumpets are its ears,
scarlet feathers sprout in line
along the knobbles of its spine
its body green, with lots
of lovely shining golden spots,
and deep within its guts resounds
a baying like an hundred hounds.

King Arthur lies in Avalon,
the knights dispersed, all dead and gone.
But sometimes on some lonely night
when restless sleepers lie abed
they hear, with an horrid fright,
far in the moon-sky overhead
uncanny and spine-chilling sounds:
the baying of an hundred hounds.

It is the lonely QUESTING BEAST
for Questing People he's requesting.
With yowls he sadly shows his pique
there's no one now plays Hide & Seek.

Poor bird!
So timid and afraid!
In dingy brown from head to tail.
You're bashful as a modest maid,
that's why they call you cringing QUAIL.
Be not so meek!
You ought to boast
of being so delightful –
roast.

This mascot in a crested coat
is **REG the REGIMENTAL GOAT**.
His beard in coiffured ringlets coil,
his dapper hooflets shine with oil;
for beauty, few things can surpass
his dainty balls of burnished brass:
each one is fitted to adorn
the dangerous points of every horn
(most goats have two, but Reg has more,
this REGIMENTAL GOAT has *four*!)

The favourite of his regiment,
for many years Reg lived content
until the day he came upon
the notice of a Ram, called Ron.
Ron was a rough and burly sheep:
his neck was thick, his bleat was deep,
he'd muscled loins and hairy heels
and horns as big as barrow wheels;
fat and foolish was his face,
his manners were a rude disgrace.

One day, it happened, as he grazed,
that Ron looked up, to stare amazed
at soldiers brave, who, marching past
with beating drum and trumpet blast
were led, with elegance and grace
by Reg, with proud and stately pace.

To show-off to his fleecy flock
the uncouth ram began to mock
with insolent and sneering bleat:
'Baaa! Silly Billy! How effete!
Call those horns, upon your head?
Why don't you wear some flowers instead?
Look at that beard! Those little curls,
Just like some silly, soppy girl's!'

☞ The mockery of this ungulate
roused our Reggie to a bate,
becoming most unkind and coarse
he bleated back: 'Mint sauce! Mint sauce!'

Now, Ronald was the sort of bloke
who could not take a personal joke
(though of others he would jest
an answer-back he did detest).
His stamped his feet, his eyeballs glared,
he swished his tail, his teeth were bared
and having lowered down his head
towards the goat he quickly sped.

He did not give poor Reg a chance
to get in a defensive stance
so when they met – a mighty CRACK –
the mascot ended on his back.

The horrid Ronnie though it funny
to trample on poor Reggie's tummy,
and finally the cruel ram dared
to graze upon the mascot's beard.

But whilst he lay there, stunned and sore
Reg heard the order: 'Halt! No more!
On your feet, Reg, to prevent
the shaming of the Regiment!'

So on his feet the mascot leapt
(something Ron did not expect).
And then the goat prepared to fight.
He truly was an awesome sight,
Ron's wives stared up in admiration
at the mascot's transformation:
the flashing of his golden balls,
his bleats, which rang like bugle calls,
his horns, each pointing like a spear.
Ronald felt a surge of fear. ☞

☛ He looked at Reg, all goggle-eyed.
'Now don't be hasty, mate!' he cried
as meek and humble as a lamb.
Too late. A mobile battering-ram
(our Reg) then hit him in the rump.
Golly! How it made that rude ram jump!
And run: over mountain, mead and dale;
his tongue hung out, his face was pale
and on his features did appear
a shamefaced, shy and sheepish air.

But what was Ronald's greatest shame
(he only had himself to blame)
and be the butt of widespread laughter:
his wives had lambs a few months after
– each lambkin looking rather weird
embellished with a goatee beard.

T'was thus that Reggie did augment
the honour of his regiment.

The **SEAL** is fat, he likes to swim,
his voice is hoarse, his eyes are dim,
of rancid fish his breathing smells,
upon a floating berg he dwells:
characteristics which appeal
to every passing lady SEAL.

Inscrutable, enigmatic, stone-faced, the **SPHINX**
has stared with cold impassion far through time
over the bleak and barren gravel plain which links
the empty desert to the town of tears.
Few know why he is there or what he thinks;
but perhaps, at twilight, there is a clue
when behind him the setting sun sinks
and evening shadows slide across his face:
slowly and sardonically, it seems
he winks.

Prone on the sea bed, not far from the shore,
the SPONGE lay and pondered and thought life a bore.
So its feelings were mixed when scooped from the sea,
squashed flat, dried out, and sold from the quay.
'Twas Miss Prism who bought it, to make contribution
as an asset to aid with her daily ablution.

Miss Prism, when bathing, sometimes it did please
to take up her SPONGE and give it a squeeze
between the round mounds which served as her knees.

Whilst doing so one bath-time, Miss P. gave a gasp
when the slippery SPONGE fell away from her grasp.
Beneath scented waters Miss Prism did grope,
but first that she found was a small cake of soap.
When she finally felt the shape of her SPONGE
towards its prone form she gave a quick lunge
– and 'neath the warm waters did splashily plunge.

The SPONGE was entangled with bits of Miss P.
'twas a long time that finally she let it go free.
'Well!' thought the SPONGE, 'it does seem to me,
that this is more fun than a life in the sea.'

See these boring
thingummy jigs?
**STICK INSECTS**,
imitating twigs:
they're very long
and frightfully thin
and grey and scaly
is their skin.
Being just like
small bits of tree
they're very difficult
to see;
another reason
they're not found
is rarely do they
move around,
they stay rooted
to the spot.
Are they amusing?
No. They're not.
They're rather odd,
but odder yet
is she who keeps one as a pet.

## The **TURKEY TROT**

Two hops to each side is how the dance starts,
then a rise and a fall on your toes,
then a pert little twitch of your nethermost parts,
whilst pecking in jerks with your nose.

Whilst trotting around, make sudden sharp stops
to peer keenly about with suspicion;
then once again start, with your double hop-hops,
then freeze, in a rigid position.

The TURKEY does this so that he and his hen
in marital bliss are connected:
so do it at Christmas, its suitable then
to get more from your bird than expected.

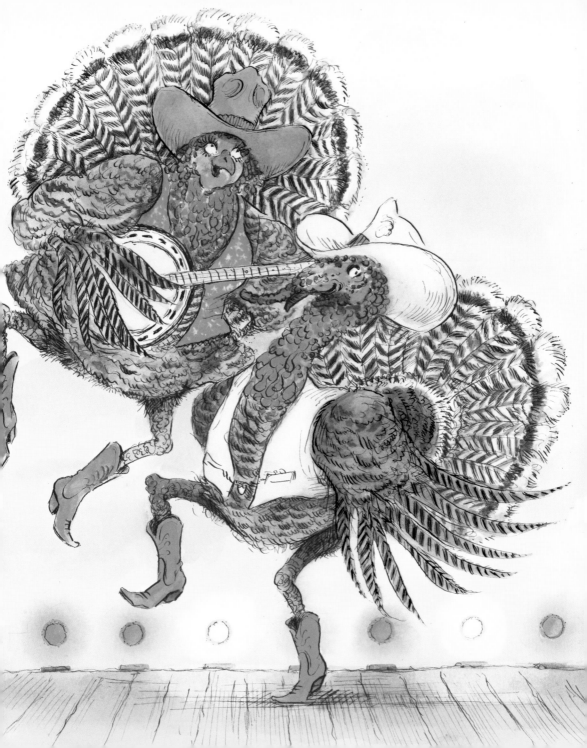

## TYRANNOSAURUS REX

you ought to please
and not annoy or vex
by making jokes
about his tiny arms
or outsize tail
or lack of dainty charms.
If tempted thus to rudeness, give a pause
to scrutinise his powerful teeth and jaws.

Who comes out at night when the flittermice fly?
It is **TAURUS** the bull, who lives high in the sky
with his body outlined by planets and stars.

When he travels through space with the god of war, Mars,
the whole world suffers with ailments and storms
and midges and microbes come out in huge swarms;
but when Venus rides with him, in the warm month of May,
the birds build their nests, and the lambs start to play.

**UMBRELLA BIRDS** inhabit woods
where rarely does it rain,
but they wear their brollies on their crests.
The reason, they explain:
there are lots and lots of horrid things
continuously shed
from the messy-mannered monkeys
in the tree-tops overhead.

The **UGLY DUCKLING**,
as a chick
was bullied and reviled
by other ducklings who would tease
this unattractive child.
But now he is a mighty swan,
so,
when he meets a duck,
from wings
and neck
and breast
and tail
its feathers
does he
pluck.

Although its body is quite hairy
bald-faced is the **U-A-KARI**.
Rather like your Uncle Fred
its nose and cheeks are very red,
it reels and staggers when it walks,
it spits and splutters when it talks.
But, unlike your uncle Fred,
it's sober when it goes to bed.

On human blood the **VAMPIRE** feeds,
with sips and sucks from lady's necks:
from fairy books that's what one reads
so that's what every girl expects
until taught better, then she knows
it sucks the blood out from their toes.

With feathered fans the **VULTURES** stroke the air
wheeling in soaring spirals to the clouds
from whence, with cold and calculating stare,
they look upon the shifting, massing crowds
of dappled shadows, drifting to and fro
across the Afric plains: the heedless herds
of earth-bound beasts that live and die below,
ignorant of the interest of the birds.

Magnificent and noble as they fly,
invisible their defects are, so far, so high;
but if one lands beside you, you will be appalled
to see the stately VULTURE is *completely* bald.

The **WEATHERCOCK**, a useful fowl,
tells us whence the wind is blowing;
he does this when it's warm and mild,
he does this when it's cold and snowing.

Whilst standing on a single leg,
high and stately on a spire,
he twiddles round from north to south:
not for a moment does he tire.

But not alone, for all around
busy and crowded is his sky:
about his head, close to the clouds,
in arabesques the swallows fly.

When autumn comes, they disappear,
with skeins of geese, they fly away;
and wistful thinks the WEATHERCOCK:
'I'll do that too, some time, some day'.

The **WITCHETTY GRUB** is quite delicious
and what is more it is very nutritious,
so don't let yourself be at all suspicious
of the twitchetty WITCHETTY GRUB.

This massive maggot, as long as a finger,
to dine upon you should not linger,
but quickly and nicely you must sing a
song to the WITCHETTY GRUB.

Go to the boozer with your mucker
for a dinkum snack of Aussie bush tucker,
don't be a whinger and let your lips pucker
when viewing the WITCHETTY GRUB.

Admire the squirms when the rubbery fellow
turns, in barbies, from white to yellow:
all together we will bellow
praise for the WITCHETTY GRUB.

Fry in chunks, or mush into mousse,
or brew it as soup in its glutinous juice;
whatever you choose, each Sheila and Bruce,
sup up your WITCHETTY GRUB!

The **WARTHOG** has a frightfully ugly face:
two massive tusks, and in the space
between, those warts.
What are the thoughts
of Mrs WARTHOG when she looks at him?
Perhaps she thinks: "at least his hips are slim,
his back is straight, his hooves are neat and trim;
(but deary me, that face is awfully grim)".

The **X-BILL**
(or Cross Bill
I'm afraid I must cheat)
has a song half between
a squeak and a tweet.
But no one can blame him
for how would YOU speak
if afflicted with such
an odd looking beak?

**XANTHOUS** was a horse from ancient Tyre;
his mother was a harpie, the Wind his sire;
not only could he fly, but he could talk.
If I'd a horse like him
I'd rather
walk.

It is a blow against the vanity
of the majority of humanity
that the rude and crude **YAHOO**
looks a bit like me and you.
It wipes the contents of its nose
upon the facings of its clothes
where, in addition, food remains
to make up lots of other stains.
It never cleans its nails or combs its hair
and little nests of fleas live where
in some of us, deodorants may be used.
Vandalism is how it keeps amused:
nothing better will it please
than breaking branches off the trees
and strewing bits of litter on the grass;
it loves the sound of breaking glass.
You can see where it sleeps at night
by the infuriating sight
in pretty country lanes
of frowsty mattresses with nasty stains

Of its faults it does not care the least:
the YAHOO is a shameless beast.

is for ZOO-KEEPER:
a hard-working man
with a broom, and a shovel, and a sanitary pan.
From the dawn of the sun, to the setting of same,
he is feeding, and sweeping, and trying to make tame
with tit-bits of herring (which pleases the seals)
and plump, juicy hamsters (the rattle-snake's meals);
the ant-eater's food he prepares with a sieve,
he mucks out the tank where the jellyfish live,
he scrapes clean the floor of the chimpanzee's cage,
he calms down the lions if they get in a rage,
he dusts out the holes of the elephant's ears,
with his hankie he mops up the crocodile's tears,
for if anything's sad – either fish, beast or bird –
he's there with a smile and encouraging word.

At dusk he goes home, where, inside of his house
there's not even a dog, nor a cat, nor a mouse;
and when he has dined, and goes to his bed, he
allows just the presence of a very old Teddy.

## Other books published by EWAG

*Nice-Looking (Essex) Girls Afloat*  ISBN 978-0-9567397-1-1  £12.95

*Essex Girls' Limericks* – Volume I  ISBN 978-0-9567397-0-4  £2.95

*Essex Girls' Limericks* – Volume II  ISBN 978-0-9567397-2-8  £3.00

Prices include postage and packing.

To order please email essexwomensadvisorygroup.com; also available from Amazon.

The Essex Girls' Limericks are two volumes which celebrate Essex Girls and some of the lovely-named places where they live. These 100 pages include girls from **Tolleshunt d'Arcy**, **Cuckingstool End** and **Bumbles Green**, old ladies from **Layer de la Haye** and **Ongar**, a naughty girl from **Cock Clarks** and a good girl from **Belchamp Walter**. These little books fits neatly into a pocket or handbag, or even a Christmas stocking.

Here are some examples:–

A lady from **Stanstead Mountfitchet**
Had a remarkable bust – she could twitch it.
*'For adjustment', she said,*
*'I stand on my head*
*That's always the best way to hitch it'.*


*'I'm in terrible need of a penny!'*
Cried a frantic old girl from **Great Henny**,
*'I've got tenners a-plenty*
*And even a twenty,*
*But of pennies – I haven't got any!'*


Whenever Sal wanted to doze
She'd hang from a beam by her toes.
The reason for that
Is her Dad was a bat –
Though her Mum was from **Beaumont-cum-Moze**.


Said the girl with a peeved Pekinese:
*'He hasn't much fun when he pees,*
*He ain't much to choose,*
*Only a couple of loos,*
*As we live on the **Isle of Two Trees**.'*


A lady from **Twizzlefoot Bridge**,
Sat numbing her bum in a fridge.
When they said to her: *'why?'*
She replied, with a sigh,
*'I've been stung in the stern by a midge'.*


Said a queasy young girl from **St Lawrence**:
*'A life on the coast's an abhorrence,*
*When I sail out to sea*
*I'm as sick as can be:*
*Not in dribs, not in drabs, but in torrents.'*


They cried: *'what a funny address!'*
To a girl from the **Isle of Foulness**.
She answered quite smugly:
*'I'm neither **Mucking** nor **Ugley**,*
*Nor go **Messing** about when I dress'.*


A wife, from **Ramsden Bellhouse**,
With anger, berated her spouse:
*'That man fondled my bum!*
*But you did nothing, by gum!*
*Do you think you're a man, or a mouse?'*


A shrimp girl who fished round **Wick Isles**
Rowed her boat – whilst standing – for miles,
If she sat on the thwarts
She'd give agonized snorts
As she suffered severely from piles.


A damsel from **Salcott-cum-Virley**
Has hair that is naturally curly.
And what makes this verse better:
She looks good in a sweater,
And her parents had christened her Shirley.